Virgin

Cheryl Baker's
LOW-CALORIE
COOK BOOK

Over **70**
nutritious and
calorie-counted
recipes

NOTES

Standard spoon measurements are used in all recipes
1 tbsp (tablespoon) = 15 ml
1 dsp (dessertspoon = 10 ml
1 tsp (teaspoon) = 5 ml
NSP = Non-starch polysaccharide
Eggs are assumed to be size 3 and pepper is freshly ground black pepper
All recipes are calculated using metric quantities, with approximate imperial equivalents given too. Use only one set of measurements.

To lose an average 900 g/2 lb per week, you need to eat 1000 kcals less than normal each day. In relation to the average intake, that means successful weight loss will occur if women consume no more than about 1200 kcals and men no more than about 1500 kcals. It is important, however, not to lose weight too quickly as this is not healthy in the short term or for long term well being. Therefore, do not go lower than 1000 kcals per day. Percentages refer to the proportion of calories.
REMEMBER All calories (kcals) calculated in these recipes include the suggested side dishes.

Acknowledgements
The following have helped me with research and nutritional information: dietitian and research nutritionist Sue Gatenby, who has a special interest in the management of obesity, and chef Sheila Crudgington, a specialist in healthy diets.

First published in Great Britain in 1996 by Virgin Books
an imprint of Virgin Publishing Limited
332 Ladbroke Grove
London W10 5AH

A catalogue record for this book is available from the British Library

ISBN: 1 85227 569 3

Printed and bound in Great Britain by DC Thomson

Art Direction and Design by Haldane Mason
Photography and Styling by Amanda Heywood
Home Economy by Kathryn Hawkins.
Photographs of Cheryl Baker by Brendan O'Sullivan

C O N T E N T S

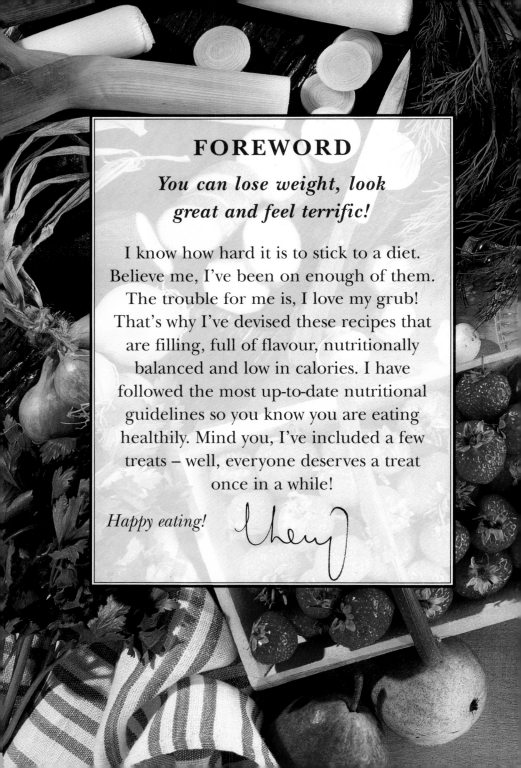

FOREWORD

You can lose weight, look great and feel terrific!

I know how hard it is to stick to a diet.
Believe me, I've been on enough of them.
The trouble for me is, I love my grub!
That's why I've devised these recipes that
are filling, full of flavour, nutritionally
balanced and low in calories. I have
followed the most up-to-date nutritional
guidelines so you know you are eating
healthily. Mind you, I've included a few
treats – well, everyone deserves a treat
once in a while!

Happy eating!

INTRODUCTION

It's not just controlling the calories in your diet that matters – it's the quality of those calories. A healthy diet is one that is low in fat, high in starchy carbohydrates and high in fibre, which usually means it's high in vitamins and minerals as well. That's a diet based on cereals and other starchy foods, and fruit and vegetables. (The fallacy that potatoes, rice and so on are fattening has long since been dispelled.) These recipes have been devised to make sure the balance of foods, on average, is just right while you are losing weight.

Each recipe has been analysed for fat, carbohydrate and fibre (NSP) for your information, and the figures given are per serving. Remember, it's the balance of your diet over several weeks that really matters and a treat now and again won't do any harm. That's why I have included some recipes that appear high in fat. Reserve those for special occasions!

The calorie (kcal) content of all recipes is inclusive of my suggested side dishes. If you want to vary the side dishes, check the calorie values on page 62 and use a food of equivalent calorie value.

All calorie counts are rounded to the nearest five. Remember to include in your daily calorie intake milk in tea and coffee, fruit and so forth. I have given you a list of some of these on page 62.

Do not go under the recommended daily calorie allowance and don't expect to lose all the excess weight in the first week. A successful diet is one that educates you to eat more sensibly over a period of time, not starve yourself for a few days! It is far better to lose 0.4–1.5 kg/1–3 lb per week on a steady, sensible diet – that way, you are more likely to keep the weight off. If you crash diet and lose 3 kg/7 lb in a week, you may find you're back on a diet in a fortnight's time!

Those of you who never exercise probably don't want to hear this, but you really should exercise at the same time – you will feel and see the benefit much sooner. Swimming, jogging or cycling a couple of times a week are very beneficial, as they burn calories as well as making you feel fitter. If you really don't have the time or the inclination for that, try walking instead of driving whenever possible.

Less fat, more carbohydrate and fibre, loads of fruit and veg, a bit of exercise and before you know it, there'll be a new you!

Nutritional information obtained from McCance and Widdowson's *The Composition of Foods*, fifth edition 1991 by RSC and MAFF. Information on Food Portion Sizes from MAFF Food Portion Sizes, second edition 1993.

BASICS

I don't think it's absolutely necessary to use home-made stocks – you can buy very good ready-made ones now. Or, of course, there's the good old stock cube; their prime ingredient is usually salt, but if time is short they will do. However, I do sometimes make stocks myself, usually when a recipe really cries out for home-made, or when I happen to have chicken, fish or beef bones left over.

BEEF OR CHICKEN STOCK
Makes about 1 litre/1³/₄ pt

♦ Wash the vegetables, then quarter the onion and cut the carrot and celery into chunks. Place all the ingredients in a large saucepan and cover with water.

♦ Bring to the boil and remove the scum. Cover the pan, leaving a gap for steam to escape. Lower the heat to a simmer and cook for about 4 hours, skimming the top every now and again.

♦ Strain the stock into another saucepan or bowl, add salt to taste and leave to cool.

♦ Remove the fat from the top. The stock is now ready to use.

Ingredients
1 large onion, unpeeled
2 carrots, unpeeled
2 celery sticks
1 kg/2¹/₄ lb beef marrowbones or a chicken carcass
1 bouquet garni
salt to taste
1.5 litres/2¹/₂ pt water

FISH STOCK
Makes about 1 litre/1³/₄ pt

♦ Chop the onion finely then put all the ingredients in a large stockpot and bring slowly to the boil, skimming often. Simmer, uncovered, for 20 minutes (no longer or the stock may become bitter), then strain and leave to cool. The stock is now ready to use.

Ingredients
1 medium onion
750 g/1¹/₂ lb fish bones, heads and tails
juice of ¹/₂ lemon
1 litre/1³/₄ pt water
10 peppercorns
large bouquet garni

VEGETABLE STOCK
Makes about 1 litre/1³/₄ pt

♦ Use vegetables such as cabbage, carrot, parsnip, leeks, tomato, onion and swede (do not allow one ingredient to overpower the rest). Boil the vegetables in the water for about 1 hour so that all the flavour is in the stock, not the vegetables.

Ingredients
500 g/1¹/₄ lb vegetables, chopped
1 litre/1³/₄ pt water

BOUQUET GARNI

♦ Either tie the herbs together with string, or cross the two leek leaves, place the herbs in the middle and tie the leek leaves together like a pouch, enclosing the herbs.

Ingredients
sprig of thyme
sprig of parsley
bay leaf
2 washed outer leaves of leek (optional)

BREAKFAST/BRUNCH

When I was young my mother tried every which way to get me to eat a breakfast. 'It'll set you up for the day,' she used to say. Needless to say, I didn't believe her then but now I'm older I know she was right. A sensible breakfast will stop you feeling tired and curb those 'elevenses' hunger pangs. I have added brunch recipes as well for those of you who, like me, enjoy a lie-in once in a while! (Remember, though, brunch replaces breakfast *and* lunch.) Either the Swiss-style Muesli or the Scrambled Egg and Tomato shown here would be a tempting way to start the day, wouldn't they?

Kcals per person: 90
Fat: 60%
Carbohydrate: 8%
NSP: 1g

Ingredients
1 egg
salt and pepper
a few snipped chives
1 tomato
whole chives, to garnish

SCRAMBLED EGG AND TOMATO
Serves **1**

❝Whenever I'm staying in an hotel, I always have this breakfast.❞

♦ Beat the egg with about 1 dessertspoon of water. Season with salt and pepper and add the snipped chives.

♦ Cook either in a saucepan on the hob until set or in the microwave. I actually find the latter method best. Use a non-metallic cup or bowl and cook the egg on Full Power for 1 minute. By now the egg will have risen and will look a bit like a soufflé. Break the egg down and continue cooking on Full Power – a few seconds at a time – until just cooked. If you overdo it, the egg will be like shredded cardboard!

♦ Meanwhile, slice the tomato in half, season and grill. Serve the dish garnished with whole chives.

A tip: You could add a slice of toast with low-fat spread: total calories would then be 210 kcal.

Kcals per person: 140
Fat: 16%
Carbohydrate: 45%
NSP: 1g

Ingredients
1/2 tsp curry powder
a shake or two of
Tabasco or chilli sauce
salt and pepper
1 tsp tomato purée
spray oil
1 lamb's kidney, cored
and sliced
1 slice of toast
(unbuttered)

DEVILLED KIDNEY TOASTIE
Serves **1**

❝This recipe could be served as a breakfast, brunch, lunch or supper!❞

♦ Put the curry powder, Tabasco or chilli sauce and tomato purée in a bowl and add salt and pepper to taste. Give it a good stir and add enough water to make a sort of runny sauce.

♦ Spray a small frying pan with the oil and heat. Add the kidney and fry gently for 2 minutes.

♦ Pour the sauce over the kidney and cook, uncovered, for a further 10 minutes, stirring occasionally to stop the kidney from sticking. If necessary, add a little more water.

♦ Serve on the slice of toast.

A tip: If the kidney is big enough or sliced thinly enough, this could stretch to two people.

SWISS-STYLE MUESLI

Serves **1**

| Kcals per person: 300 |
| Fat: 28% |
| Carbohydrate: 61% |
| NSP: 4g |

When I eventually did start eating breakfasts, if I was in a hurry I just used to throw some oats in a bowl with a bit of sugar and milk. In those days, porridge was cooked, never eaten raw. My mum thought I was stark raving mad! Nowadays, we all seem to have a packet of muesli in the cupboard. Funny how times change, isn't it?

♦ Put the oats in a bowl with the water and leave overnight.
♦ The following morning, mix all the other ingredients in with the oats, sweeten to taste and serve.

A tip: The measurement for the milk is approximate – you may add a little more or less for your preferred consistency.

Ingredients
2 tbsp rolled oats
50 ml/2 fl oz water
1/2 dessert apple, chopped
1 heaped tbsp sultanas, washed
1 tsp chopped hazelnuts
100 ml/3 1/2 fl oz skimmed milk
artificial sweetener

KEDGEREE

Serves **1**

| Kcals per person: 370 |
| Fat: 8% |
| Carbohydrate: 55% |
| NSP: 5g |

I think I'm right in saying that kedgeree started life in India as a breakfast dish for the British in the days of the Raj. Wherever it started, I'm quite happy for it to finish on my plate! However, because of the calorie content I really think this should be a brunch, don't you?

♦ In a saucepan, poach the haddock in seasoned milk for 4 minutes. Rest for 1 minute (the haddock, I mean – not you!).
♦ Remove the haddock from the pan and flake the flesh, being careful to remove all the bones and the skin. Cover the haddock and keep warm.
♦ Add the rice, onion and turmeric or curry powder to the juices from the haddock and boil for 2 minutes. Add the haddock and frozen peas and boil for a further 2 minutes until the juices are absorbed.
♦ Transfer to a plate and sprinkle with chopped parsley. Serve with sliced raw tomatoes.

Ingredients
100 g/4 oz smoked haddock
salt and pepper
100 ml/3 1/2 fl oz skimmed milk
100 g/4 oz cooked rice
1 small onion, chopped
1/4 tsp turmeric or curry powder
1 tbsp frozen peas
chopped parsley

STARTERS AND LIGHT LUNCHES

I don't really think it's necessary to have a starter unless you're having guests over for dinner. For myself, I would rather have more on my dinner plate! Consequently, most of these recipes are for 2–4 people, but all of them can be divided or multiplied as necessary. Alternatively, you could try any of these recipes as a light lunch instead. Shown here are Chinese Chicken and Leek Rolls and Cheryl's Ensalata Tricolore. I think they look – well, good enough to eat!

Kcals per person: 105
Fat: 42%
Carbohydrate: 26%
NSP: 1g

Ingredients
10 g/¹⁄₄ oz butter
150 g/5 oz chicken livers
1 clove garlic, crushed
¹⁄₂ small onion, finely chopped
1 tsp English mustard
1 tbsp chopped parsley
salt and pepper
watercress
cherry tomatoes

CHICKEN LIVER PATE
Serves **4**

❝Here's an old favourite – serve it with crispy melba toast (page 45). ❞

♦ Melt the butter in a frying pan and add the chicken livers, garlic and onion. Fry over a medium heat for 5 minutes, stirring continuously. Remove the chicken liver mixture from the pan and leave to cool a little.

♦ Add the mustard, parsley and seasoning to the livers and either whizz in an electric blender or press through a sieve.

♦ Spoon the pâté into 4 small pots, cover with lightly oiled clingfilm or kitchen foil and put something heavy on top to weight the pâté down. Refrigerate overnight.

♦ Garnish with watercress and cherry tomatoes and serve with melba toast. You can offer your guests butter if you like, but the toast will be so crisp it will probably break. Personally, I don't think pâté needs butter anyway.

Kcals per person: 95
Fat: 21%
Carbohydrate: 9%
NSP: 0g

Ingredients
2 skinned chicken breast fillets
1 leek, quartered lengthwise
2 tbsp soy sauce
1 tsp grated fresh root ginger
1 clove garlic, crushed
1 tbsp dry sherry or rice wine
1 tsp clear honey
chives, to garnish

CHINESE CHICKEN AND LEEK ROLLS
Serves **4**

❝This starter looks quite impressive and tastes even better than it looks.❞

♦ Lay the chicken fillets out on a work surface and place a leek quarter at one end of each, lengthwise. Roll up and secure with toothpicks or a skewer.

♦ If there is any leek left over, chop finely and place in a bowl with the soy sauce, ginger, garlic, dry sherry or rice wine and clear honey. Mix these ingredients thoroughly or whizz in a processor for a few seconds.

♦ Pour over the chicken rolls and leave to marinate for 1 hour.

♦ Wrap the chicken rolls in kitchen foil, place in a steamer and cook for 20 minutes, or until the chicken is cooked through.

♦ Remove the toothpicks or skewers and slice the chicken rolls into rounds about 2 cm/³⁄₄ inch thick. Garnish with whole chives and serve with extra soy sauce for dipping.

WARM SALAD
Serves 2

Kcals per person: 110
Fat: 53%
Carbohydrate: 33%
NSP: 1g

❝I tried this salad in a Belgian restaurant in Covent Garden. It was so nice I thought I should share it with you! ❞

♦ Preheat the oven to 230°C/450°F/Gas Mark 8. Prepare the salad leaves, tearing the larger ones into pieces, and place in a salad bowl. Skin the tomato and chop it finely, along with the olives. Trim the bacon of all rind and fat.

♦ Remove the crusts from the bread and cut the bread into small dice. Bake in the oven until golden.

♦ Dry-fry or grill the bacon, then cut into thin strips. Put the tomato, olives, garlic and seasoning in a jar with the oil-free vinaigrette. Shake vigorously.

♦ Sprinkle the warm toasted bread cubes and bacon strips over the salad leaves, pour the dressing over and serve.

Ingredients
mixed salad leaves, eg lamb's lettuce, frisée, rocket, radicchio, spinach, chicory, cos lettuce
.....
1 tomato
.....
4 pitted black olives
.....
1 rasher of back bacon
.....
1 thin slice of bread
.....
1 clove garlic, crushed
.....
salt and pepper
.....
3 tbsp oil-free vinaigrette

CHERYL'S ENSALATA TRICOLORE
Serves 4

Kcals per person: 55
Fat: 48%
Carbohydrate: 17%
NSP: 0g

❝One of my favourite starters when I go to an Italian restaurant is Ensalata Tricolore, or three-coloured salad. It is the colours of the Italian flag, green, white and red – avocado, mozzarella cheese and tomato. A drizzle of olive oil and some freshly milled black pepper and – mmm, I'm there now! However, if lose weight you must, then the following version is the one for you.❞

♦ Overlap the cucumber, mozzarella and tomato slices around the plate. Tear the basil into small pieces and sprinkle over, followed by the pepper.

♦ I love olive oil with this dish so I would rather do without altogether than use a substitute. However, this is a matter entirely for your own taste.

A tip: By the way, get the mozzarella in bags of fluid, not the block pizza type.

Ingredients
1/2 unpeeled cucumber, washed and sliced
.....
1 half-fat mozzarella cheese, thinly sliced
.....
2 large tomatoes, sliced
.....
2 sprigs of fresh basil
.....
pepper
.....
oil-free dressing (optional)

STUFFED MUSHROOMS
Serves 1

This is a nice informal starter when friends come round for dinner – just multiply the ingredients. Equally, it will make a filling lunch.

Kcals per person: 340
Fat: 51%
Carbohydrate: 28%
NSP: 2g

Ingredients
2 large field mushrooms
1 rasher of back bacon, all rind and fat removed (optional)
½ small onion, finely chopped
½ slice of bread, crumbed
1 tsp butter or margarine
15 g/½ oz flour
75ml/3 fl oz skimmed milk
25 g/1 oz low-fat Cheddar
salt and pepper
sprigs of parsley

♦ Preheat the oven to 200°C/400°F/Gas Mark 6. Wipe the mushrooms with a damp cloth and remove the stalks. Chop the stalks finely.
♦ Chop the bacon finely and dry-fry with the onion for 2 minutes.
♦ In a bowl, mix the breadcrumbs with the bacon, onion and mushroom stalks and heap into the field mushrooms.
♦ Melt the butter or margarine in a small saucepan, add the flour and cook, stirring, for 1 minute.
♦ Gradually add the milk and cook for a further minute on a low simmer. The sauce should be quite thick.
♦ Add the cheese and seasoning and stir until the cheese has melted.
♦ Place the mushrooms on a rack over a baking tray and spoon cheese sauce into the centre of the mushrooms (do not pour too much sauce over as it will drip during cooking.) Bake in the oven for 20 minutes, or until the cheese is bubbling. Serve garnished with parsley.

TUNA BEAN SALAD
Serves 4

There are many types of bean you could make this salad with – flageolet, red kidney, haricot, or a mixture of all of them!

Kcals per person: 170
Fat: 7%
Carbohydrate: 48%
NSP: 7g

Ingredients
1 red pepper
150 g/5 oz French beans
1 small can (approx 175 g/6 oz) tuna in brine, drained
400 g/14 oz can butter beans (or other), strained
2 spring onions, chopped
salt and pepper
2 tbsp chopped fresh coriander

♦ Cut the red pepper in half lengthwise and place skin-side up under a hot grill.
♦ When the skin has blackened, remove the pepper and leave to cool a little. Remove the skin and chop the pepper finely.
♦ Top and tail the French beans, cut them in half and cook in boiling water for 4–5 minutes. (They will still be quite crunchy – if you prefer more 'give' cook them a little longer.)
♦ In a bowl, break the tuna into pieces and add the butter beans, spring onions, red pepper and cooled French beans. Season well and toss together until thoroughly mixed (not too vigorously or the tuna will look mushy.)
♦ Sprinkle with fresh coriander and serve.

A tip: You could pour on a little oil-free dressing if you like.

Kcals per person: 160
Fat: 10%
Carbohydrate: 55%
NSP: 1g

Ingredients
200 g/7 oz raw prawns,
shelled
....
2 cloves garlic, finely
sliced
....
I fresh chilli, finely sliced,
or I tsp dried crushed
chilli or ½ tsp hot chilli
powder
....
pepper
....
approx 500 ml/18 fl oz
stock, home-made (page
9) or use 1 vegetable
stock cube
....
sprigs of parsley

HOT SPANISH PRAWNS
Serves 4

This is a real favourite of mine. The first time I ever had Gambas Al Pil Pil, as it is called in Spain, was in Paco's Tapas Bar in Arroyo De La Miel on the Costa del Sol. They were divine! Unfortunately for us dieters, though, they are usually cooked in nothing but lots of olive oil. This is a slimmers' version.

♦ Place the prawns, garlic and chilli into 4 earthenware dishes.
♦ Season with pepper, cover with stock and grill on high for 3–4 minutes, turning the prawns over once. Make sure they are opaque and cooked thoroughly. (You probably won't need to use all the stock, just enough to cover the prawns.)
♦ Alternatively, put in the microwave on Full Power for 2 minutes per dish.
♦ Garnish with parsley and serve with crusty bread for dipping. You can have half a slice if you're good!

A tip: Wear rubber gloves when you slice the chilli 'cos it doesn't half sting when you forget and rub your eyes!

Kcals per person: 95
Fat: 13%
Carbohydrate: 29%
NSP: 1g

Ingredients
100 g/4 oz low-fat
yoghurt
....
juice of ½ lemon
....
1 tbsp tomato ketchup
....
200 g/7 oz cooked and
peeled prawns
....
½ iceberg lettuce
....
100 g/4 oz fresh
tomatoes
....
100 g/4 oz cucumber
....
2 spring onions
....
½ red pepper
....
paprika or chopped herbs

PRAWN SALAD COCKTAIL
Serves 4

This is a very easy variation on a favourite starter. Although I have given you measured ingredients here, they aren't cast in stone – you can add or subtract any ingredient you like and alter the amounts to suit your taste. By all means give your guests brown bread and butter, but you don't really want it, do you?!

♦ Combine the yoghurt, lemon juice and tomato ketchup thoroughly to make the cocktail sauce. Stir the prawns into the sauce.
♦ Chop the lettuce, tomatoes, cucumber, spring onions and red pepper finely. Mix them together and divide the mixture between 4 glass sundae dishes.
♦ Top with prawn cocktail and sprinkle with either a large pinch of paprika or chopped fresh herbs such as coriander, basil or parsley.

A tip: One whole prawn or a wedge of lemon over the side of the dish always looks good.

TROPICAL CRAB
Serves 2

❛This delicious crab recipe is so easy – and very low in calories. It's simplest to use canned crabmeat, though of course you can use fresh if you prefer.❜

♦ Halve the papaya lengthwise, remove the seeds and fill the cavity with crabmeat.
♦ Season to taste with pepper and then sprinkle with a little lime juice and some chopped fresh parsley. Finally, garnish with lime wedges to serve.

A tip: If the papaya rocks on the plate, use shredded lettuce as a base for it to sit on.

Kcals per person: 85
Fat: 6%
Carbohydrate: 47%
NSP: 3g

Ingredients
1 fresh papaya
100 g/4 oz crabmeat
pepper
a little lime juice
chopped parsley

MUSSELS MARINIERE
Serves 4

❛I have always loved seafood. Being brought up in the East End of London, I was weaned on cockles, whelks, jellied eels and winkles, but one seafood I just couldn't sink my teeth into was the mussel. Until . . . one day when Steve, my husband, was thoroughly enjoying Moules Marinière in our favourite restaurant, Luigi's. They looked so nice that I tried one – and it was delicious! I am now a mussel convert! I have seen mussels measured in several different ways – pints, kilos, pounds – so here I have tried to cover all possibilities!❜

♦ Scrub the mussels thoroughly and remove the beards.
♦ Heat the butter in a frying pan and fry the onion, garlic and celery gently for 2 minutes.
♦ Transfer the onion mixture to a very large saucepan, add the white wine and water and bring to the boil.
♦ Add the mussels, season with plenty of pepper, cover the saucepan and boil for 5 minutes.
♦ Serve in big soup bowls sprinkled with parsley, with a spare dish for the shells – and a finger bowl!
♦ This dish works quite well in the microwave – place all the ingredients in a large microwave dish and cook on Full Power for 2 minutes.

A tip: Any mussels that have not opened should be discarded.

Kcals per person: 205
Fat: 26%
Carbohydrate: 6%
NSP: 0g

Ingredients
1 kg/2¼ lb/2.25 litres/ 4 pt mussels
15 g/½ oz butter
1 medium onion, finely chopped
2 cloves garlic, crushed
1 celery stick, finely chopped
225 ml/8 fl oz liquid made up of 1 glass dry white wine and water
pepper
chopped parsley

FRENCH ONION SOUP
Serves **4**

❝The first time I had French onion soup was in a posh restaurant abroad somewhere and I was very impressed with it. I hope you will be too.❞

Kcals per person: 110
Fat: 15%
Carbohydrate: 60%
NSP: 1g

Ingredients
300 g/11 oz onions

900 ml/1½ pt beef or vegetable stock, home-made (page 9) or use 1 stock cube

1 bouquet garni (page 9 or use a sachet)

salt and pepper

4 slices French bread cut from a baton (small stick)

40 g/1½ oz Edam cheese, grated

♦ Slice the onions thinly and put them into a saucepan with the stock, bouquet garni and seasoning to taste.

♦ Bring to the boil then reduce to a simmer and cook, covered, for 20 minutes.

♦ Meanwhile, toast the bread on both sides.

♦ Ladle the soup into individual soup bowls, float a slice of toast on each and sprinkle with a little cheese.

♦ Place the soup bowls under a preheated grill until the cheese bubbles and serve.

A tip: Take care – it's easy to burn your mouth on this soup!

GREEN SUMMER SOUP
Serves **4**

❝There's nothing nicer on a cold winter's day than a steaming mug of soup – but have you ever tried cold soup on a hot day? Asking around, I discovered that not many people have. I suppose it's a bit like asking if you've ever tried warm ice-cream! It's something I've grown to love, though, and it's really worth trying.❞

Kcals per person: 60
Fat: 18%
Carbohydrate: 21%
NSP: 1g

Ingredients
1 cucumber

1 bunch of watercress

225 g/8 oz cottage cheese

600 ml/1 pt chicken or vegetable stock, home-made (page 9) or use 1 stock cube

large pinch of dried mustard or curry powder

♦ Chop the cucumber roughly and wash the watercress thoroughly.

♦ Put all the ingredients save 1 sprig of watercress into a blender and whizz until smooth. Pour into a tureen or jug and chill in the refrigerator.

♦ Serve with ice cubes if you like, and decorate with a sprig of watercress.

Kcals per person: 115
Fat: 22%
Carbohydrate: 43%
NSP: 1g

Ingredients
1 tsp sunflower oil
1 small onion, finely chopped
1 clove garlic, finely chopped
1 small courgette, grated
1 small carrot, grated
100 g/4 oz curd cheese
100 g/4 oz cottage cheese
2 tsp finely chopped fresh herbs
salt and pepper

VEGETABLE CHEESE PATE
Serves **4**

❝Have I mentioned that I love cheese? All cheese, no matter how strong or mild, no matter how hard or soft. It's something I really miss when I'm dieting. This starter is the next best thing – mild but with a lovely flavour from the added vegetables and herbs. ❞

♦ Heat the oil in a frying pan and lightly fry the onion and garlic until softened.

♦ Add the grated courgette and carrot and continue cooking for a further 4–5 minutes, until all the ingredients are tender.

♦ In a bowl, thoroughly mix the two cheeses together, then add the vegetables and fresh herbs such as basil, parsley, coriander or rosemary. Season to taste.

♦ Transfer to ramekin dishes or similar and put in the refrigerator for 1 hour to set.

♦ Serve with melba toast (page 45) and sticks of celery.

Kcals per person: 55
Fat: 3%
Carbohydrate: 86%
NSP: 2g

Ingredients
¼ iceberg lettuce, shredded
1 orange, peeled
1 grapefruit, peeled
a few mint leaves
50 ml/2 fl oz Florida orange juice

FLORIDA SALAD
Serves **2**

❝I filmed in Florida for a TV programme, and one of the items featured was at a fruit juice processing plant. I am now completely hooked on Florida juices. I saw the acres and acres of oranges and grapefruit and witnessed the transformation from fruit to juice – the most delicious juice I had ever tasted. It is not always possible to buy fresh Florida fruit but it is possible to buy Florida juices.❞

♦ Arrange the shredded lettuce on 2 plates. Break the orange and grapefruit into segments and arrange on the lettuce in alternate segments.

♦ Tear the mint leaves and sprinkle over the orange and grapefruit.

♦ Pour the orange juice over, chill and serve.

A tip: If you want to bother you can remove the skin from the fruit segments, although I wouldn't go to that much trouble!

CRUDITES
Serves as many as you like!

❝*I like sinking my teeth into something crisp, such as a juicy apple or some fresh raw vegetables. Fruit and veg can make a nice light starter for a meal or perhaps when you're hit by a snack attack! Go easy on the dips, though, if it's just a snack.*❞

Fruit and veg, for instance:
celery, courgette, peppers (any or all colours)
cucumber, tomatoes, carrot, chicory
spring onion, mushrooms
cauliflower and broccoli florets
apple, pear, grapes, orange, etc.

♦ Cut the vegetables into finger-pieces.
♦ Combine each dip thoroughly and chill them in the refrigerator before serving.

A tip: Watch the chilli in the Salsa! They vary in strength, so add a little at a time to taste – and wear rubber gloves!

TZATZIKI

Kcals: 95

Ingredients
150 g/5 oz low-calorie yoghurt
1/2 cucumber, peeled, deseeded and grated
1/2 tsp dried oregano
salt and pepper

WATERCRESS DIP

Kcals: 60

Ingredients
150 g/5 oz low-calorie yoghurt
1/2 bunch watercress, finely chopped

SALSA

Kcals: 70

Ingredients
3 firm tomatoes, finely chopped
1 small onion, finely chopped
1 tbsp fresh coriander, finely chopped
1 green chilli, finely chopped
juice of 1/2 lime
1/2 tsp salt
pepper

THOUSAND ISLAND YOGHURT DIP

Kcals: 280

Ingredients
150 g/5 oz low-calorie yoghurt
1 tbsp tomato ketchup
1 chopped dsp each of green olives, spring onion, pimentos or red pepper
1 hard-boiled egg, chopped
dash of Tabasco sauce
salt and pepper

MAIN COURSES

These recipes are designed to fill you up
without fattening you up! The calorie
(kcal) counts given for each recipe
include my suggested side dishes. I have
given some quite basic recipes as well as a
few more unusual ones to add a bit of
variety to your diet. If you choose to have
a starter and/or pud with your main
course, remember to take into account the
extra calories you've treated yourself to
and adjust the rest of your day's intake
accordingly. On the right, Hot Chicken
and Mango Sauce and Stuffed Cabbage
Leaves tempt the tastebuds!

Kcals per person: 365
Fat: 20%
Carbohydrate: 45%
NSP: 2g

Ingredients
4 chicken breasts, boned
and skinned

Marinade
1 medium onion
1 cm/½ inch fresh root
ginger
1 red chilli or ½ tsp dried
red chillies
2 cloves garlic, crushed
salt and pepper
juice of 1 lemon or lime
1 tbsp olive oil

Mango sauce
1 ripe mango
juice of ½ lime
2 tbsp low-calorie
yoghurt
salt and pepper

HOT CHICKEN AND MANGO SAUCE
Serves **4**

This is quite a spicy dish, but the mango sauce sort of cools it down. I like hot, spicy food, but if you prefer you could omit the chilli.

♦ Preheat the oven to 200°C/400°F/Gas Mark 6.

♦ To make the marinade, chop the onion finely and grate the fresh root ginger. If you are using a fresh red chilli, chop it finely and take care to discard all the seeds, which are very hot. Put all the marinade ingredients into a screwtop jar, twist the lid on firmly and give the marinade a good shake.

♦ Score the chicken breasts with a sharp knife, place in a bowl or dish (don't worry if they are folded) and coat with the marinade. Leave for 1 hour.

♦ Lay the breasts flat on a baking tray and roast in the middle of the oven for 20 minutes.

♦ To make the mango sauce, mash the mango well or push through a sieve. Add the other ingredients and mix well.

♦ Serve the chicken breasts with the mango sauce and a small portion of rice per person (see page 62). Garnish with chopped parsley and a lime slice.

Kcals per person: 345
Fat: 16%
Carbohydrate: 41%
NSP: 0g

Ingredients
1 chicken breast fillet
juice of 1 lime
100 g/4 oz low-fat
yoghurt
1 tsp tikka paste
chopped fresh coriander

CHICKEN TIKKA
Serves **1**

This is a good one for the barbecue as well as the grill.

♦ Skin the chicken breast and cut it into cubes.

♦ Mix the lime juice, low-fat yoghurt and tikka paste together thoroughly, add the chicken and coat evenly. Leave to marinate for 1 hour.

♦ Push on to skewers and grill for 10 minutes, turning the kebabs every few minutes.

♦ Serve with salad and a small portion of rice (see page 62) sprinkled with fresh coriander.

SHREDDED SWEET 'N' SOUR CHICKEN

Serves 4

Kcals per person: 280
Fat: 18%
Carbohydrate: 30%
NSP: 2g

I cannot deny it – I adore Chinese food. I think the cooking methods are wonderful and the use of spices and flavourings imaginative. One of the all-time favourites of Chinese cuisine is 'sweet and sour', so here's one for you.

♦ Slice the chicken as thinly as possible, place in a bowl with the spring onions and garlic, season well and pour the sherry over. Make sure the chicken is coated with the marinade and set aside for 15 minutes.

♦ Pour the chicken, garlic and spring onions into a hot non-stick frying pan and cook on quite a high heat for 3–4 minutes, until the chicken is cooked. (If it is sticking to the pan, add a little water.)

♦ Put the remaining ingredients in a saucepan, mix thoroughly and bring to the boil. Reduce to a simmer for 3 minutes.

♦ Stir the chicken and spring onions into the sauce.

♦ Serve with a 150 g/5 oz portion of boiled Chinese noodles.

Ingredients

450 g/1 lb chicken off the bone
4 spring onions, chopped
2 cloves garlic
salt and pepper
1 tbsp dry sherry
2 tbsp soy sauce
2 tbsp artificial sweetener
2 tbsp wine vinegar
2 tsp chilli sauce
2 tbsp tomato purée

CHICKEN CHASSEUR

Serves 4

Kcals per person: 315
Fat: 14%
Carbohydrate: 36%
NSP: 5g

I do love entertaining. The only trouble is, it can be difficult to do when you're on a diet. Here's a favourite recipe and I bet none of your guests will realize it's low in calories as well as delicious!

♦ Preheat the oven to 200°C/400°F/Gas Mark 6. Chop the shallots, slice the mushrooms and cook them in a little stock for 2–3 minutes on a low simmer.

♦ Add the wine and boil until it has reduced by half.

♦ Add the tomatoes, bouquet garni and remaining stock and season to taste (do not add salt if you have used a stock cube).

♦ Place the chicken breasts in an ovenproof dish and pour the chasseur sauce over them. Cover with a lid or foil and bake in the oven for 30 minutes.

♦ Serve with a medium portion of new potatoes per person (see page 62) and mange tout.

Ingredients

6 shallots
100 g/4 oz mushrooms
250 ml/8 fl oz chicken stock, home-made (page 9) or use 1 chicken stock cube
1 glass dry white wine
4 tomatoes, skinned and chopped
1 bouquet garni (page 9 or use a sachet)
salt and pepper
4 chicken breasts, boned and skinned

Kcals per person: 370	
Fat: 30%	
Carbohydrate: 51%	
NSP: 1g	

Ingredients
spray oil

75 g/3 oz lean pork fillet

4 spring onions, chopped

2 cloves garlic, chopped

2 cm/³/₄ inch fresh root
ginger, grated

500 g/1¹/₄ lb mixed
vegetables, eg carrots,
broccoli, mange tout,
peppers, green beans or
cauliflower, cut into thin
strips or small florets

2 tbsp soy sauce

PORK AND VEGETABLE STIR-FRY
Serves **2**

❝The reason I like stir-frying is it's so quick. The preparation usually takes longer than the cooking and eating put together – but it's worth it! This recipe includes quite a lot of vegetables and not much meat. The result is still delicious.❞

♦ Spray a wok or large frying pan with oil and heat. Cut the pork into strips. Throw the pork, spring onions, garlic and ginger into the wok or pan and fry, stirring continuously, for 2 minutes.

♦ Add all the other ingredients and continue stir-frying for a further 2 minutes. If it seems to be drying out, add a little water.

♦ Garnish with chives and serve with a small portion of boiled rice (see page 62).

♦ This will give you quite crunchy vegetables, which is how I like them. Obviously, if you prefer a bit more 'give', cook them a little longer. Bear in mind that mange tout take very little cooking, so add them 1–2 minutes after the denser vegetables such as carrots. Add a third clove of garlic if you're feeling adventurous!

Kcals per person: 500	
Fat: 32%	
Carbohydrate: 31%	
NSP: 9g	

Ingredients
2 lamb cutlets

1 sprig of fresh rosemary
or ¹/₂ tsp dried

50 g/2 oz mushrooms

1 leek

150 ml/¹/₄ pt beef stock,
home-made (page 9) or
use 1 stock cube

1 tsp wholegrain mustard

a couple of dashes of
Worcestershire sauce

1 dsp tomato purée

salt and pepper

LAMB CUTLETS IN LEEK AND MUSHROOM GRAVY
Serves **1**

❝If any two vegetables should be married, they are the leek and the mushroom! They seem to go so perfectly together, and they complement lamb beautifully. Lamb is quite a fatty meat, so this recipe has a higher calorie content – don't eat it too often!❞

♦ Trim the fat from the cutlets and dry-fry them with the rosemary in a hot frying pan for 2–3 minutes each side. Remove from the pan and keep warm.

♦ Slice the mushrooms and leek finely and add to the pan, scraping up any meat residue. You may need to pour a little of the stock in if the vegetables are sticking. Cook for 2 minutes.

♦ Add all the other ingredients and bring to the boil until the gravy is slightly thickened.

♦ Serve the cutlets with gravy poured round them, accompanied by spinach and a medium portion of mashed or new boiled potatoes (see page 62).

Kcals per person: 430
Fat: 16%
Carbohydrate: 48%
NSP: 9g

Ingredients
1/2 green pepper
1/2 red pepper
2 courgettes
2 tomatoes
1 small onion
100 g/4 oz lean rump steak
1 clove garlic, crushed
250 ml/8 fl oz beef stock, home-made (page 9) or use 1 stock cube
salt and pepper
chopped parsley

BEEF RATATOUILLE
Serves 1

Ratatouille is a very famous French dish which is usually made with vegetables alone. I have added steak in this version, although you could choose to omit it or use chicken instead. (Remember, though, that if you do this the calorie content will be different.)

♦ Slice the peppers and courgettes and skin and slice the tomatoes. Chop the onion.

♦ Cut the lean rump steak into thin strips (this is easiest to do when it is almost frozen). Dry-fry the steak and garlic over a high heat for just 2 minutes.

♦ Add the prepared vegetables and beef stock to the pan and season to taste. Mix well. Bring to the boil, then cover the pan and simmer for 30 minutes.

♦ Sprinkle the ratatouille with chopped parsley and serve with a small jacket potato (see page 62).

Kcals per person: 445
Fat: 29%
Carbohydrate: 48%
NSP: 8g

Ingredients
1 small onion
50 g/2 oz mushrooms
1/4 red or green pepper
1 celery stick
1 carrot
227 g/8 oz can tomatoes
75 g/3 oz lean minced beef
1 clove garlic, crushed
large pinch of dried oregano
1 beef stock cube
1 tbsp tomato purée
salt and pepper
shredded basil or chopped parsley

SPAGHETTI BOLOGNESE
Serves 1–2

I absolutely adore pasta and Steve, my husband, makes a great Bolognese sauce. It isn't typical of Italy, but it's good when you're dieting as the vegetables add bulk so that you feel you've had a good hearty meal but without as many calories as a normal Bolognese.

♦ Chop all the vegetables into small cubes. Dry-fry the beef for 2 minutes, breaking down any lumps, until the beef has browned a little all over.

♦ Add all other ingredients except the basil or parsley with enough water to make a thick soup consistency. Bring to the boil, then reduce to a simmer and cook for 20 minutes, stirring occasionally.

♦ Serve poured on top of a small portion of spaghetti (see page 62) with a sprinkling of basil or parsley for colour. Unfortunately, parmesan cheese is very high in calories so I wouldn't if I were you!

A tip: If the pasta is cooked before the sauce, don't keep it warm – it will stick together. Strain it under the cold tap as soon as it is cooked and keep it in the refrigerator. Then plunge it into a saucepan of boiling water for 30 seconds when you're ready for it. Oh, and make sure it's well drained or else you will have a very watery dinner!

GRILLED KIDNEYS AND RICE
Serves **1**

Kcals per person: 315
Fat: 25%
Carbohydrate: 51%
NSP: 4g

❛*Unfortunately Steve doesn't like liver or kidneys. However, I do . . .*❜

♦ Remove any fat from the outside of the kidneys. With the rounded side upwards, slit lengthwise to the core and peel off the outer membrane. Leaving the core intact, open out the kidney butterfly-fashion.

♦ Mix the thyme and a good grind of pepper into the olive oil and coat the kidneys and mushrooms.

♦ Place the kidneys and mushrooms under a medium-hot grill and cook for 5–6 minutes, turning occasionally until the kidneys are cooked through.

♦ Meanwhile, gently cook the onion and tomato in a little water for 3 minutes.

♦ Stir the onion and tomato into the piping-hot cooked rice, place the kidneys and mushrooms on top and serve, sprinkled with a little parsley for colour.

Ingredients
2 lamb's kidneys
½ tsp dried thyme
pepper
1 tsp olive oil
4 large mushrooms
1 small onion, finely chopped
2 tomatoes, skinned and chopped
100 g/4 oz boiled rice, hot
chopped parsley

TOMATO, MUSHROOM AND LIVER BAKE
Serves **1**

Kcals per person: 370
Fat: 35%
Carbohydrate: 31%
NSP: 8g

❛*This is a recipe that even Steve eats, as it's sort of disguised!*❜

♦ Preheat the oven to 200°C/400°F/Gas Mark 6. Finely slice the tomatoes and mushrooms and place in an ovenproof dish.

♦ Cut the liver into strips and lay them on top of the tomatoes and mushrooms.

♦ Season to taste, then top with a mixture of breadcrumbs, cheese and mixed herbs. Bake in the oven for 30 minutes.

♦ Serve with green beans.

Ingredients
200 g/7 oz tomatoes
200 g/7 oz mushrooms
75 g/3 oz liver
salt and pepper
50 g/2 oz brown breadcrumbs
25 g/1 oz low-fat Cheddar cheese, grated
½ tsp dried mixed herbs

Kcals per person: 430

Fat: 14%

Carbohydrate: 53%

NSP: 8g

Ingredients
100 g/ 4 oz beef fillet
1 large onion
4 large tomatoes
4 courgettes
spray oil or ½ tsp vegetable oil
1 tsp dry English mustard
1 dsp low-fat fromage frais or yoghurt
1 tsp honey
2 cloves garlic, crushed
salt and pepper

BEEF AND VEG LAYER
Serves 1

❝Ooh, this one's lovely!❞

♦ Preheat the oven to 180°C/350°F/Gas Mark 4. Slice the beef thinly into at least 4 slices. Slice the onion, tomatoes and courgettes, again thinly.

♦ Oil a frying pan and heat until very hot, then flash fry the beef for a few seconds on each side to seal it.

♦ Mix the mustard, fromage frais or yoghurt, honey and garlic to a paste and spread over the beef. Season to taste.

♦ Place 2 beef slices in a baking dish. Cover with slices of onion, tomato and then courgette. Place the remaining beef slices on top, repeat the layers of vegetables and brush the final layer of courgette with a little oil. Place in the oven and bake for 20 minutes.

♦ Serve accompanied by a small portion of potatoes (see page 62) and a side salad.

Kcals per person: 420

Fat: 37%

Carbohydrate: 53%

NSP: 6g

Ingredients
450 g/1 lb potatoes
450 g/1 lb cooking apples
1 tbsp artificial sweetener
1 tsp salt
1 tsp vinegar
25 g/1 oz low-fat spread
pepper
4 long or 8 short frankfurters, whole or chopped, heated

POTATO AND APPLE WITH FRANKFURTERS
Serves 4

❝This is one I tried on my children's cookery programme, Eggs 'n' Baker. It was an adaptation of a German recipe called Heaven and Earth. It tasted so good, I thought it should be shared with the grown-ups!❞

♦ Peel and cube the potatoes and peel, core and slice the apples. Place the potatoes, apples, artificial sweetener, salt and vinegar in a large saucepan and just cover with water. Bring to the boil and simmer for 10 minutes, or until the potatoes are cooked.

♦ Drain well and mash with the low-fat spread, season with more salt (if necessary) and pepper and spoon into a warmed serving dish. Serve with the heated frankfurters on top and a garnish of poached apple slices and a sprig of parsley.

Kcals per person: 350
Fat: 14%
Carbohydrate: 51%
NSP: 2g

Ingredients

300 g/11 oz smoked haddock

100 g/4 oz plain flour

pinch of salt

2 eggs

250 ml/8 fl oz skimmed milk

spray oil

100 g/ 4 oz low-fat fromage frais

¼ tsp turmeric

pepper

chopped parsley

sprig of dill

POACHED HADDOCK CREPES
Serves **4**

❝*This is a delightful meal. If possible, buy haddock that hasn't been dyed yellow – the natural creamy yellow of smoked haddock is far nicer.*❞

♦ Skin the haddock and poach gently in a little water for 10 minutes, until cooked. Flake the flesh, removing any bones.

♦ To make the crêpe batter, sieve the flour and salt into a mixing bowl, make a well in the centre and break the eggs into it. Using a whisk or fork, start to incorporate the flour into the eggs, gradually adding the milk. Keep whisking until the mixture is free of lumps and has the consistency of thin cream.

♦ Spray a frying pan with oil and heat until smoking. Reduce the heat to medium and pour 2 tablespoons of the batter into the pan. Swirl the batter around to coat the pan and cook for about 30 seconds, or until you can lift the sides of the crêpe and the underneath is golden. Toss or turn the crêpe and cook the other side for a few seconds, then turn out on to a warm plate.

♦ Continue until all the batter is used, remembering to oil the pan each time. (Keep the other crêpes warm and cover them with foil or a damp tea towel or they will dry out.)

♦ Mix the haddock with the fromage frais, turmeric and pepper to taste. Spoon into the crêpes and roll up. Garnish with parsley and dill and serve with a tomato salad and a chunk of crusty bread.

Kcals per person: 375
Fat: 10%
Carbohydrate: 55%
NSP: 4g

Ingredients

30g/1¼ oz long-grain rice

pinch of turmeric

1 crisp dessert apple

juice of 1 lime

½ tsp curry powder

salt and pepper

150 g/5 oz low-fat yoghurt

150g/5 oz cooked shelled prawns

chopped fresh coriander

CURRIED PRAWN AND RICE SALAD
Serves **1**

❝*The first time I ever tried Indian food, I had prawn curry and rice. Here's a cold variation, good for lunch or dinner on a summer's day.*❞

♦ Boil the rice with the turmeric for the recommended time on the rice packaging.

♦ Chop the apple into small cubes and coat in lime juice to stop discoloration as well as to add flavour.

♦ Mix the curry powder and seasoning into the yoghurt. Add the apple cubes.

♦ When the rice is cooked, drain and cool under cold running water. Drain again thoroughly or your salad will be very watery.

♦ Mix all the ingredients together, sprinkle with chopped fresh coriander and nosh! Serve with cucumber and tomato.

FISH SHISH
Serves 1

Kcals per person: 395
Fat: 20%
Carbohydrate: 45%
NSP: 5g

❝ *Shish, of course, should be meat. I've used poetic licence on this one because I like the title! Monkfish is pricy, so just substitute another firm-fleshed variety of fish if you want a more economical dish.* ❞

♦ Mix all the marinade ingredients in a screwtop jar and give it a good shake!

♦ Cut the monkfish into chunks. Put all the seafood in a bowl and coat in marinade. Leave for 1–2 hours.

♦ Slice the courgette and cut the onion and red pepper into chunks. Push all the ingredients alternately on to skewers. Brush with marinade and grill or barbecue until the seafood is opaque and the vegetables are browned.

♦ Serve on a bed of rice (small portion – see page 62), sprinkled with your favourite herb – mine is coriander!

Ingredients
75 g/3 oz monkfish
75 g/3 oz raw prawns
1 courgette
1 onion
¼ red pepper
6 button mushrooms
Marinade
juice of 1 lemon
2 tsp olive oil
salt and pepper
large pinch of paprika

TROPICAL FISH
Serves 4

Kcals per person: 340
Fat: 11%
Carbohydrate: 54%
NSP: 7g

❝ *I used to sing in a wonderful restaurant called the Elephant on the River and was fortunate enough to be fed and watered there every night! I still go back there now and again, and I'm pleased to say that one of my favourites on the menu back in 1978 (giving away my age here!) is still a favourite today. This version is perhaps not quite to the standard of the Elephant on the River, but it's still pretty good!* ❞

♦ Preheat the oven to 190°C/375°F/Gas Mark 5. Lay the plaice fillets out flat and cover half of each fillet with slices of banana.

♦ Spread the sweet pickle over the banana and fold the other halves of the fillets over to cover the banana and sweet pickle. Fasten together with toothpicks and place in an ovenproof dish.

♦ Pour the milk over the fish and cover. Cook in the oven for 15 minutes.

♦ Serve with a medium portion of new potatoes (see page 62) and plenty of green beans and carrots.

Ingredients
4 fillets of plaice
1 banana, sliced
4 tsp sweet pickle
300 ml/½ pt skimmed milk

MOCK LOBSTER KEBABS
Serves 1

Kcals per person: 280
Fat: 8%
Carbohydrate: 57%
NSP: 6g

Ingredients
1 clove garlic, crushed
large sprig of fresh
coriander, chopped
1 tbsp tomato purée
1 tbsp low-fat yoghurt
juice of ½ lime
salt and pepper
150 g/6 oz monkfish
sprig of coriander, to
garnish

Monkfish is extremely ugly with its enormous head, but its flavour more than compensates for its appearance! Make sure it is thoroughly cooked, as it tends to be tough if undercooked. Monkfish tends to shrink more than other fish, so make the chunks really chunky!

♦ Soak 2–3 wooden skewers for 30 minutes (or use metal ones if you prefer). Meanwhile, combine the garlic, coriander, tomato purée, yoghurt, lime juice and seasoning to taste.

♦ Cut the fish into chunks and coat with the yoghurt mixture. Leave to marinate for 30 minutes.

♦ Push the fish chunks on to skewers and grill under a low heat for 10 minutes, turning and basting with any yoghurt that is left, until the fish is cooked.

♦ Garnish with coriander and serve with a small portion of rice (see page 62) and plenty of steamed carrots and broccoli.

FISH, LEEK AND BROCCOLI PIE
Serves 2

Kcals per person: 380
Fat: 13%
Carbohydrate: 54%
NSP: 9g

Ingredients
125 g/4½ oz leeks
125 g/4½ oz broccoli
125 g/4½ oz white fish
100 g/4 oz low-fat
fromage frais
salt and pepper
75 g/3 oz stale brown
breadcrumbs
25 g/1 oz low-fat
Cheddar cheese, grated
sprig of dill, to garnish

This is not a pie in the true sense of the word – more of a crumble, I suppose.

♦ Preheat the oven to 200°C/400°F/Gas Mark 6. Slice the leeks finely and cut the broccoli into small florets. Flake the fish or cut it into chunks.

♦ Steam or boil the leeks and broccoli for 3 minutes, then drain.

♦ Combine the leeks, broccoli and fish with the fromage frais, season well and pour into an ovenproof dish.

♦ Combine the breadcrumbs with the Cheddar cheese and sprinkle on to the fish mixture.

♦ Bake in the oven for 6 minutes until the breadcrumbs are toasted.

♦ Garnish with dill and serve with spinach and a medium portion of new potatoes or Jersey Royals (see page 62).

Kcals per person: 345
Fat: 9%
Carbohydrate: 56%
NSP: 4g

Ingredients
2 shallots
2 spring onions
500 g/1¼ lb potatoes
170 g/6 oz can tuna in brine, drained
50 g/2 oz sweetcorn
100 g/4 oz low-fat fromage frais
salt and pepper
25 g/1 oz low-fat Cheddar cheese, grated

QUICK TUNA BAKE
Serves 2

❝There's so much more you can do with the humble can of tuna than bung it in a sandwich.❞

♦ Preheat the oven to 230°C/450°F/Gas Mark 8. Chop the shallots and spring onions finely.

♦ Peel the potatoes and cut them into chunks. Boil the potatoes for 20 minutes until cooked, then mash them.

♦ Thoroughly mix together the tuna, shallots, spring onions, sweetcorn and fromage frais. Season to taste.

♦ Pour the tuna mixture into an ovenproof dish and top with mashed potato. Sprinkle the grated cheese on top.

♦ Bake in the centre of the oven for 20–30 minutes, until golden on top. (Keep an eye on it to make sure the cheese doesn't burn.)

♦ Serve with a tomato salad.

Kcals per person: 330
Fat: 10%
Carbohydrate: 74%
NSP: 6g

Ingredients
1 packet dried low-calorie mushroom soup
1 small onion, finely chopped
2 cloves garlic, crushed
1 celery stick, chopped
100 g/ 4 oz mushrooms, sliced
sprig of basil, shredded

TAGLIATELLE WITH MUSHROOM SAUCE
Serves 1

❝I have yet to meet a chef who doesn't cheat occasionally. If it makes your life a little easier, then do it – just don't tell anybody! See if you can spot where I have cheated in this pasta recipe.❞

♦ Make up the soup according to the manufacturer's instructions on the packet.

♦ In a saucepan, gently poach the onion, garlic and celery in a little water for 2–3 minutes.

♦ Add the mushrooms to the pan and cook for a further 2 minutes, adding water whenever necessary.

♦ Pour the mushroom soup into the pan and stir gently.

♦ Taste for seasoning, pour on to a medium portion of pasta (see page 62) and sprinkle with basil.

Did you spot it?!!

A tip: You don't have to use tagliatelle – any similar pasta will do. Needless to say, fresh is best, if you can find it – or make it!

STUFFED CABBAGE LEAVES
Serves 1

Kcals per person: 440
Fat: 15%
Carbohydrate: 47%
NSP: 9g

❛*Like most children, I always used to refuse point blank to eat my greens! However, my mum used to be very crafty and make her food look so intriguing that I just had to eat it to find out exactly what it contained! This is a recipe that's grown up with me.*❜

♦ Remove the stalks from the cabbage leaves. Cover the cabbage leaves with the chicken stock and leave for 2 minutes, until limp (the cabbage leaves, I mean – not you!). Drain the leaves, reserving the chicken stock.

♦ Chop the chicken and spring onions finely and mix with all the other ingredients. Fill the cabbage leaves, wrapping them around the mixture to make a parcel (do not overfill). Hold together with cocktail sticks.

♦ In a saucepan, bring the stock back to the boil and poach the cabbage parcels for 5 minutes.

♦ Garnish with strips of spring onion and serve with a small jacket potato and two or three canned plum tomatoes. (The tomato juice goes beautifully with the parcels.)

Ingredients
2 large cabbage leaves
250 ml/8 fl oz boiling chicken stock, home-made (page 9) or use 1 chicken stock cube
100 g/4 oz cooked chicken
2 spring onions
25 g/ 1 oz brown breadcrumbs (about 1 medium slice)
salt and pepper
1/2 tsp dill seeds (optional)

SPANISH OMELETTE
Serves 1

Kcals per person: 260
Fat: 44%
Carbohydrate: 30%
NSP: 1g

❛*This is a very easy recipe that uses up any leftover potatoes you may have in the fridge. A true Spanish omelette just has potato in it, like this one here. However, if you prefer a bit more crunch to your omelettes, try adding some finely chopped onion and red pepper.*❜

♦ First chop the cooked potato roughly.

♦ Put a non-stick pan over a high heat and spray with a little oil.

♦ Whisk the eggs with 1 tablespoon of cold water and season with salt, pepper and a pinch of paprika.

♦ Pour the egg mixture into the hot pan, add the potato, turn the heat down low and cover the pan. Cook until set, then turn out upside down.

♦ Serve with a salad garnish.

Ingredients
1 medium cooked potato (100 g/4 oz)
spray oil
2 eggs
salt and pepper
paprika

VEGETABLE MEDLEY
Serves 2

Kcals per person: 460
Fat: 25%
Carbohydrate: 56%
NSP: 4g

❝I am not a vegetarian, but I absolutely adore vegetables and am quite happy to go without meat or fish once in a while. This is a good substantial meal for 2.❞

Ingredients

450 g/1 lb courgettes
450 g/1 lb carrots
100 g/4 oz mushrooms
25 g/1 oz butter
25 g/1 oz flour
300 ml/½ pt skimmed milk
100 g/4 oz low-fat soft cheese
salt and pepper
1 tbsp breadcrumbs

Quick Tomato Sauce
1 tsp cornflour
2 tbsp tomato ketchup
100 ml/3½ fl oz apple juice

♦ Slice the carrots and courgettes thinly and cook in separate pans of boiling water until just tender. Drain.

♦ Slice the mushrooms thinly and fry in half the butter. Drain.

♦ In a flameproof dish, layer half the courgettes, all the carrot and all the mushrooms, then top with the remaining courgettes.

♦ Melt the remaining butter in a small saucepan, add the flour and cook for 1–2 minutes. Stir in the milk and continue stirring until the sauce thickens. Cook for a further 2 minutes, then add the cheese and season to taste.

♦ Pour the cheese sauce over the vegetables and sprinkle the top with the breadcrumbs. Place under the grill and brown lightly.

♦ To make the Quick Tomato Sauce, make a thin paste with the cornflour and a little water. Thoroughly mix the ketchup into the apple juice and heat in a small saucepan. Add the cornflour mixture and bring to the boil, stirring constantly.

♦ Serve the Vegetable Medley accompanied by the Quick Tomato Sauce and a mixed salad.

ITALIAN-STYLE TOFU
Serves 2

Kcals per person: 315
Fat: 41%
Carbohydrate: 25%
NSP: 4g

❝Tofu is often used in Japanese cuisine. It is extremely high in protein with little or no calorie content – great when you're on a diet! The only trouble with tofu is that it's quite bland and tasteless. If it is marinated or cooked in a sauce, however, it's an entirely different story. ❞

Ingredients

2 × 225 g/8 oz packets of tofu
salt and pepper
450 g/1 lb can tomatoes
2 tsp olive oil
1 medium onion, sliced
1 clove garlic, chopped
1 tbsp tomato purée
50 ml/2 fl oz dry white wine
50 ml/2 fl oz vegetable stock
1 bay leaf
flour for dusting
spray oil

♦ Sprinkle the tofu with salt and pepper and leave to stand until any fluid comes out. Drain in a colander. Chop the tomatoes.

♦ In a heavy saucepan, heat the olive oil and fry the onion for 2 minutes. Add the garlic and tomato purée and cook for a further 2 minutes. Add the wine, stock, bay leaf and chopped tomatoes, bring to the boil and reduce to a simmer.

♦ Cut the tofu into 1 cm/½ inch slices and dust with flour.

♦ Spray or brush a frying pan with a little oil and heat. Fry the tofu until golden, being careful not to let it stick to the pan.

♦ Slide the tofu into the tomato sauce and simmer over a low heat until the sauce thickens.

♦ Garnish with chopped parsley and serve with French beans and a small portion of pasta quills (see page 62).

RED VEG
Serves 1

I've always thought that beetroot is a much undervalued vegetable – it has a lovely sweet flavour and the colour is just beautiful. In this dish, the fromage frais makes it look and taste nicer still.

♦ Peel the cooked beetroot and cut it into sticks. Mix the lemon juice with the fromage frais. Place on top of the beetroot and sprinkle with paprika.

♦ Serve hot or cold.

Kcals per person: 95
Fat: 3%
Carbohydrate: 57%
NSP: 1½ g

Ingredients
1 medium cooked beetroot (50 g/2 oz)
1 tsp lemon juice
100 g/4 oz low-fat fromage frais
paprika

SUNRISE VEGETABLES
Serves 1

The apple juice in this recipe gives the vegetables a lovely sweet/sharp flavour.

♦ Peel the parsnips, turnips or swede and carrots and cut them into batons (fat matchsticks).

♦ In a small saucepan, bring the apple juice to a simmer and poach the mixed vegetables for 3–5 minutes.

A tip: At 3 minutes the vegetables will still be quite crunchy, which is how I like them. At 5 minutes they will be softer, of course!

Kcals per person: 125
Fat: 8%
Carbohydrate: 87%
NSP: 5g

Ingredients
50 g/2 oz parsnips
50 g/2 oz turnips or swede
50 g/2 oz carrots
150 ml/¼ pt apple juice

CREAMY LETTUCE
Serves 1

Lettuce isn't only for salads, you know!

♦ Wash the lettuce and shred it finely. Wipe the mushrooms with a damp cloth and slice them finely.

♦ Heat the stock or water in a pan and add the mushroom slices. (If you are using water you will need to add salt and pepper too). Cook for 1 minute, then add the lettuce.

♦ Cook for 1 more minute, then stir in the yoghurt and serve.

Kcals per person: 45
Fat: 26%
Carbohydrate: 42%
NSP: 2g

Ingredients
1 soft-leaf lettuce
4 medium-sized mushrooms
2 tbsp chicken or vegetable stock, or water
1 tbsp low-fat yoghurt

SCRUMPY VEG
Serves 1

❛Aah, this takes me back to Somerset . . .❜

Kcals per person: 100
Fat: 3%
Carbohydrate: 75%
NSP: 3g

Ingredients
2 medium potatoes
2 medium carrots
100 ml/3½ fl oz dry cider
salt and pepper
1 tsp chopped fresh parsley

♦ Preheat the oven to 200°C/400°F/Gas Mark 6. Peel the potatoes and carrots and slice them very finely. Layer the potato and carrot in an ovenproof dish.

♦ Pour the cider over the potato and carrot and season to taste. Cover and bake for 40 minutes.

♦ Sprinkle with parsley and serve.

MELBA TOAST
Serves 4

Kcals per person: 20
Fat: 7%
Carbohydrate: 18%
NSP: 0g

Ingredients
1 thick-cut slice of white bread

♦ Remove the crust from the bread. Toast the bread until golden on both sides.

♦ Using a sharp knife, carefully slice through the toast horizontally, cut into 8 triangles and toast the white side until golden.

BOMBAY POTATOES
Serves 2

❛If ever I eat an Indian meal, I always have Bombay Potatoes as a side dish. I love it!❜

Kcals per person: 90
Fat: 21%
Carbohydrate: 72%
NSP: 2g

Ingredients
1 large potato
1 small onion
1 tsp oil
½ tsp chilli powder
½ tsp ground turmeric
1 cm/½ inch fresh root ginger, grated
150 ml/¼ pt water
1 tsp garam masala
salt
a few sprigs of fresh coriander

♦ Cut the potato into medium-sized chunks and boil them until they are just tender.

♦ Chop the onion very finely. Heat the oil in a pan and fry the onion until golden.

♦ Add the chilli powder, turmeric and ginger and continue to fry for a further 1–2 minutes, stirring continuously. Add the water and bring to a simmer.

♦ Stir in the potatoes, cover the pan and cook until the sauce has thickened – about 10–15 minutes.

♦ Finally, sprinkle with garam masala, stir and add salt to taste. Garnish with fresh coriander and serve.

DESSERTS

I've never been a great lover of desserts myself – I prefer a cheeseboard, which of course is taboo when you're on a diet! I always make a pud when I have a dinner party, though, which usually means I end up eating the pud *and* the cheese! If you're entertaining, or if you've just got a sweet tooth, here are some puds that won't pile on the pounds. Shown right are Boozy Apple Crumble and Pears in Reddish Wine. Low-fat yoghurt and imagination are a great alternative to custard!

DESSERTS

Kcals per person: 120
Fat: 3%
Carbohydrate: 79%
NSP: 2g

Ingredients
4 oranges
2 tsp dried ginger
500 ml/18 fl oz
unsweetened orange
juice

BAKED ORANGE
Serves 4

❝This one's a favourite of my father-in-law.❞

♦ Preheat the oven to 200°C/400°F/Gas Mark 6. Peel the oranges and slice them thinly.

♦ Place in an ovenproof dish, overlapping the slices.

♦ Sprinkle the orange slices with dried ginger, pour the orange juice over and bake for 20 minutes. Serve hot or cold with, if you like, 4 tablespoons of very low-fat fromage frais on top.

Kcals per person: 140
Fat: 10%
Carbohydrate: 58%
NSP: 3g

Ingredients
200 g/7 oz gooseberries
2 egg whites
artificial liquid sweetener
to taste
300 g/11 oz low-fat
yoghurt
mint leaves, to decorate

GOOSEBERRY FOOL
Serves 2

❝I like this one because it isn't too sweet – depending how much sweetener you put in it, I suppose. It looks best in glass sundae dishes. Although goosigogs (as I prefer to call them!) are the traditional fruit for this dish, you could try any other fruit and it will work equally well.❞

♦ Place the gooseberries in a saucepan and cover. Cook on a low heat for 15 minutes.

♦ Leave to cool a little, then either push them through a sieve or whizz in a blender until smooth.

♦ Using an electric or hand whisk, whisk the egg whites into peaks.

♦ Add liquid sweetener to the gooseberries. Fold in the yoghurt and egg whites until thoroughly mixed. Chill before serving, decorated with mint leaves.

A tip: As this recipe contains raw egg, I would not recommend it to pregnant women, the elderly or the very young.

BOOZY APPLE CRUMBLE

Serves 4

Kcals per person: 165
Fat: 3%
Carbohydrate: 65%
NSP: 2g

❝This is a nice one for the winter. Apple crumble must rate as one of the great British puds, and here I've given it some extra zing.❞

♦ Preheat the oven to 190°C/375°F/Gas Mark 5. Peel and core the apples and chop roughly. Place in a saucepan with the cider, lemon zest and cinnamon. Bring to the boil, then reduce to a simmer and cook for 5 minutes.

♦ Using a slotted spoon, transfer the apple pieces to an ovenproof dish. Taste the flavoured cider, sweeten accordingly and pour over the apple pieces.

♦ Mix the crushed cornflakes with the breadcrumbs and sprinkle over the apple.

♦ Bake for 15–20 minutes or until the topping is crisp.

♦ Serve with low-fat yoghurt, decorated with mint sprigs.

Ingredients

500 g/1¼ lb cooking apples

150 ml/¼ pt strong cider

grated zest of ½ lemon

½ tsp ground cinnamon

artificial sweetener (powder or liquid)

25 g/1 oz crushed cornflakes

75 g/3 oz brown breadcrumbs (about 3 slices)

GINGERED MELON BALLS

Serves 2

Kcals per person: 85
Fat: 3%
Carbohydrate: 91%
NSP: 1g

❝If you've over-indulged on the main course, here's a very light dessert with which to end your meal. Alternatively, it could be a starter.❞

♦ Halve the melon and scoop out the flesh, using a melon baller. (If you do not have a melon baller, remove the flesh carefully with a spoon or knife and cut into cubes.)

♦ Place the melon balls in a serving dish with the grapes and pour the apple juice over.

♦ Toss lightly and place in the refrigerator to chill.

♦ Dust with ginger and serve.

A tip: You can usually find a choice of dessert melons on sale these days, and any type will do for this recipe. Canteloupe and Charentais have salmony-coloured flesh, while Ogen and Galia have green – it's up to you which you think goes best with black grapes!

Ingredients

1 dessert melon

about 12 black seedless grapes

50 ml/2 fl oz apple juice

½ tsp ground ginger

PINEAPPLE WHIRL

Serves **2**

*❝When I was a little girl, pineapple juice was my absolute
favourite drink. Consequently, I love this dessert.❞*

♦ Make up the gelatine following the packet instructions, using
heated pineapple juice instead of water.
♦ Leave it to cool, then add the remaining juice, the yoghurt and
sweetener to taste.
♦ Either whisk in the food colouring (slowly or it will be dark
yellow!) and pour into serving dishes, or pour the pineapple
yoghurt mixture into serving dishes first, then swirl food colouring
in with a cocktail stick to make a pattern.
♦ Place in the refrigerator for 1 hour to set.

Kcals per person: 200
Fat: 3%
Carbohydrate: 78%
NSP: 0g

Ingredients
1 packet (11g/¹/₄ oz)
gelatine
150 ml/¹/₄ pt pineapple
juice
150 ml/¹/₄ pt low-fat plain
yoghurt
artificial sweetener
(powder or liquid)
yellow food colouring

CARAMELIZED HOT FRUIT

Serves **1**

❝This dessert should be served straight from the grill.❞

♦ Halve the nectarine or peach, remove the stone and slice the flesh.
♦ Hull the strawberries and cut them in half.
♦ Cut the banana into thick diagonal slices. Toss them in a little
lemon juice to prevent them discolouring.
♦ Arrange the fruit alternately on a round heat-resistant plate, spoon
the fromage frais over and sprinkle with the sugar.
♦ Place under a preheated hot grill and cook until bubbling and
golden. Serve decorated with a mint sprig.

Kcals per person: 140
Fat: 3%
Carbohydrate: 79%
NSP: 2g

Ingredients
1 nectarine or peach
4 strawberries
¹/₂ banana
a little lemon juice
2 tbsp low-fat fromage
frais
1 tsp demerara sugar
mint sprig, to decorate

Kcals per person: 125
Fat: 2%
Carbohydrate: 75%
NSP: 4g

Ingredients
4 firm dessert pears
250 ml/8 fl oz orange juice
1 glass of red wine
1 tsp ground cinnamon
artificial liquid sweetener
150 g/5 oz low-fat fromage frais
orange zest, to decorate

PEARS IN REDDISH WINE
Serves 4

❝*Pears in red wine is an old favourite. Well, here's a low-calorie cheats' version!*❞

♦ Preheat the oven to 200°C/400°F/Gas Mark 6. Peel, core and halve the pears. Lay them cut side down in a round ovenproof dish, preferably in a pattern so they look nice!

♦ Pour the orange juice and red wine over the pears and sprinkle with cinnamon. Bake for 30 minutes or until the pears are tender.

♦ Taste the juice and sweeten it if necessary. Chill before serving with fromage frais arranged in the centre of the dish, topped decoratively with mint leaves.

Kcals per person: 230
Fat: 39%
Carbohydrate: 33%
NSP: 1g

Ingredients
6 low-sugar digestive biscuits
25 g/1 oz half-fat margarine
225 g/8 oz cottage cheese, sieved
100 g/4 oz low-fat yoghurt
juice and grated zest of 1 lemon
artificial sweetener (powder or liquid)
1 egg, separated
1 sachet gelatine (11 g/¹/₄ oz)

CHEESECAKE
Serves 4

❝*Here's one of the most popular desserts. It is quite high in calories, so go easy on the rest of your meal. Mind you, I'm a great believer in a treat every now and then.*❞

♦ Place the digestive biscuits in a polythene bag and then bash 'em with a rolling pin!

♦ Mix the margarine and biscuit crumbs together well, and press into the base of a lightly greased 18 cm/7 inch flan tin with a removable base.

♦ Mix the cottage cheese, yoghurt and lemon juice and zest together, and sweeten to taste. Beat the egg yolk and add to the mixture.

♦ Make up the gelatine according to the packet instructions, leave to cool a little and stir into the cheesecake mixture. Refrigerate for 1 hour until thickened.

♦ Whisk the egg white until it stands in peaks and fold into the cheesecake mixture.

♦ Spoon on to the biscuit base and refrigerate for a further 2–3 hours before serving. You could simply decorate the cheesecake with a twist of lemon, or cover it with fruit if you prefer. Raspberries or kiwi fruit (or both) would look good.

A tip: As this recipe includes raw egg, I would not advise the cheesecake be given to very young children, the elderly or pregnant women.

FRUIT SALAD
Serves 4

Kcals per person: 100
Fat: 3%
Carbohydrate: 81%
NSP: 2g

53

❝*A pretty safe bet when dieting is to go for the fruit salad, which can sometimes be a bit boring. Here's an idea which will make it more interesting. For a start, buy (or pick!) some interesting fruit. Go for colour as well as taste, and try types of fruit you haven't tasted before. You will need about 500 g/1¼ lb.*❞

◆ To make the fruit syrup, mix all the ingredients together.
◆ Prepare the fruit – peel if necessary, wash and hull, remove pips and so on – and chop into bite-sized pieces.
◆ Place the fruit into a large glass bowl and pour the fruit syrup over. Cover with clingfilm and refrigerate for 2–3 hours before serving so that the fruit can soak in the juice.

A tip: You don't have to use orange juice. I actually prefer pineapple juice – it's up to you.

Ingredients
500 g/1¼ lb assorted fruit

Fruit syrup
275 ml/11 fl oz orange juice
1 tbsp Cointreau
½ tsp ground ginger
artificial sweetener to taste

FROSTED BOWL OF FRUIT
Serves 4

Kcals per person: 85
Fat: 4%
Carbohydrate: 89%
NSP: 3g

❝*You can have a really low-calorie pud but make it look so special that everybody wants some – like this one.*❞

◆ Using a sharp knife, cut the melon through horizontally in a saw-toothed pattern. Scoop out the pips.
◆ Using a melon baller, remove the melon flesh, taking care not to damage the melon rind. (If you do not have a melon baller, use a spoon or knife carefully and cut into cubes).
◆ Hull the strawberries and cut them in half. Peel and slice the kiwi fruit. Chop the apple into cubes.
◆ Mix all the fruit together and pile into the melon shells. Chill in the refrigerator and dust with icing sugar just before serving.

A tip: Of course, you can use any other fruit if you prefer.

Ingredients
2 dessert melons (Ogen, Cantaloupe, Charentais etc.)
100 g/4 oz strawberries
2 kiwi fruit
1 medium apple
100 g/4 oz green seedless grapes
100 g/4 oz black seedless grapes
1 tsp icing sugar

ENTERTAINING

I love entertaining, and would rather have
a dinner party than a knees-up any day. I
think six or eight is the ideal number, and
practically all of the recipes in this book
could easily be adapted for more people.
The real secret of a successful dinner
party is planning a menu of recipes that
work well together. I have devised a few
for you here which are interesting and
varied – pictured right are Poached
Salmon Crêpes, Gooseberry Fool and
Florida Salad. Each menu is approximately
600 calories per serving in total. I wonder
whether your guests will realize they are
eating a low-calorie healthy meal that
is also delicious?!

Summer Menu

Florida Salad	(page 24)	60 kcal
Poached Haddock Crêpes	(page 36)	350 kçal
Gooseberry Fool	(page 48)	140 kcal
		TOTAL 550 kcal

or

Green Summer Soup	(page 22)	60 kcal
Mock Lobster Kebabs	(page 38)	280 kcal
Cheesecake	(page 52)	230 kcal
		TOTAL 570 kcal

Winter Menu

French Onion Soup	(page 22)	110 kcal
Chicken Chasseur	(page 29)	315 kcal
Caramelized Hot Fruit	(page 50)	140 kcal
		TOTAL 565 kcal

or

Warm Salad	(page 17)	110 kcal
Fish, Leek and Broccoli Pie	(page 38)	380 kcal
Pears in Reddish Wine	(page 52)	125 kcal
		TOTAL 615 kcal

Vegetarian Menu

Vegetable Cheese Pâté	(page 24)	115 kcal
Italian-style Tofu	(page 42)	315 kcal
Boozy Apple Crumble	(page 49)	165 kcal
		TOTAL 595 kcal

Informal Menu

Chicken Liver Pâté with Melba Toast	(page 16/45)	110 kcal
Potato and Apple with Frankfurters	(page 34)	420 kcal
Fruit Salad	(page 53)	100 kcal
		TOTAL 630 kcal

....

Oriental Menu

Chinese Chicken and Leek Rolls	(page 16)	95 kcal
Pork and Vegetable Stir-fry	(page 30)	370 kcal
Gingered Melon Balls	(page 49)	85 kcal
		TOTAL 550 kcal

....

Spanish-style Tapas

With tapas, you don't have individual portions for each person. You put everything on the table, starters and main courses, and everyone dips in and has a little of each. If all the suggested dishes here were used for a table of 4 people, they would amount to approximately 515 kcal per person. Finish with a Frosted Bowl of Fruit (page 53) at 85 kcal per person.

Hot Spanish Prawns	(page 20)	160 kcal
Beef Ratatouille	(page 32)	430 kcal
Spanish Omelette	(page 41)	260 kcal
Cheryl's Ensalata Tricolore	(page 17)	55 kcal
Curried Prawn and Rice Salad	(page 36)	375 kcal
Quick Tuna Bake	(page 40)	345 kcal
Beef and Vegetable Layer	(page 34)	430 kcal

SAVOURY AND SWEET TREATS

I believe that the worst thing when you're on a diet is denying yourself any treats. If you really feel that you *must* have a square of chocolate, then go ahead and have it – otherwise, you'll only hate the diet, lose heart and give up altogether. It's far better to indulge yourself a little every now and again, so I've devised a few treats you might like to try that are very quick and easy to make. Mind you, they're not supposed to be eaten all at once – though Chewy Pear Slices and Chocolate-dipped Fruit (right) could tempt you to it!

Kcals per piece: 70
Fat: 16%
Carbohydrate: 19%
NSP: 1g

Ingredients
1 spring onion
2 tbsp cottage cheese
1/2 tsp yeast extract
1 celery stick

CHEESY CELERY
Makes **8**

♦ Chop the spring onion finely. Mix the cottage cheese, the yeast extract and the chopped spring onion together and cram the mixture into the celery stick. Chop into 2.5 cm/1 inch pieces and eat when you feel the need!

Kcals per person: 95
Fat: 62%
Carbohydrate: 5%
NSP: 1g

Ingredients
1 hard-boiled egg
1 tsp low-fat yoghurt
1/2 tsp curry powder
salt and pepper

DEVILLED EGGS
Serves **1**

♦ Slice the egg in half lengthwise and remove the yolk. Mash the yolk with the yoghurt, curry powder and seasoning and place back into the egg white.

Kcals per biscuit: 34
Fat: 12%
Carbohydrate: 77%
NSP: 6g

Ingredients
200 g/7 oz cooked potatoes
2 tsp fresh chopped mixed herbs, or 1 tsp dried
50 g/2 oz rolled oats
1/4 tsp paprika
salt and pepper
spray oil

HERBED POTATO BISCUITS
Makes **10**

♦ Mash the potatoes and add the herbs, oats, paprika and seasoning to taste.

♦ Using your hands, knead into a smooth ball. On a lightly floured surface, roll out to about 1 cm/1/2 inch thick. Cut out shapes with a biscuit cutter or upturned eggcup.

♦ Lightly spray a frying pan with oil, heat the pan and then fry the herbed potato biscuits for 2 minutes on each side until they are browned and crisp.

A tip: If you would like a more fiery biscuit, you could replace the paprika with dry mustard powder. Another variation is to use just one herb instead of mixed herbs.

SEASONED POPCORN

Serves 1

♦ Put the popcorn into a medium-sized saucepan (you'll be amazed how it expands!), place on a fairly high heat and shake the pan continuously until all the corn has popped. Season the popcorn and eat while still warm.

Kcals per person: 120
Fat: 14%
Carbohydrate: 82%
NSP: 0g

Ingredients
a handful of unpopped corn
salt and pepper
paprika or herbs

BANANA MILK SHAKE

Serves 2

♦ Whizz the milk, banana and a few drops of vanilla essence with a handful of ice-cubes in the blender. Decorate with a sprig of mint before serving.

Kcals per shake: 130
Fat: 3%
Carbohydrate: 70%
NSP: 1/2 g

Ingredients
300 ml/1/2 pt skimmed milk
1/2 banana
vanilla essence

CHOCOLATE-DIPPED FRUIT

Makes approx 20

♦ Melt the chocolate in a bain-marie or in a heat-resistant bowl placed over a pan of simmering water.
♦ Dip the fruit into the chocolate (not too much, now!) and place on a baking sheet lined with greaseproof paper. Place in the refrigerator to set.

Kcals per piece: 30
Fat: 48%
Carbohydrate: 48%
NSP: 1g

Ingredients
any fruit, as long as it is dry
100 g/4 oz plain chocolate

CHEWY PEAR SLICES

♦ Preheat the oven to 240°C/475°F/Gas Mark 9. Slice a pear thinly, spread evenly on a baking tray and bake in the oven for 15 minutes. Leave to cool on a wire rack. (If you leave them on the baking tray, the sugar in the pear slices will stick them fast!) Store in a lidded container in the refrigerator and nibble when you get the urge. Apples are equally good treated in the same way.

Kcals per person: 60
Fat: 2%
Carbohydrate: 94%
NSP: 2g

Ingredients
1 dessert pear

CALORIE COUNTER

Food or drink	Quantity	Kcals
MILK		
(whole) in 1 cup of tea/coffee	25 ml	17
(whole) in 1 mug of tea/coffee	30 ml	20
(semi-skimmed) in 1 cup of tea/coffee	30 ml	14
(semi-skimmed) in 1 mug of tea/coffee	40 ml	18
(skimmed) in 1 cup of tea/coffee	35 ml	12
(skimmed) in 1 mug of tea/coffee	50 ml	17
(semi-skimmed) average glass	200 ml	92
(semi-skimmed) in cereal	100 ml	46

N.B. *We tend to put less whole milk in tea/coffee than we do skimmed or semi-skimmed, which is why the amounts vary.*

Food or drink	Quantity	Kcals
SUGAR		
1 level teaspoon	4 g	16
1 heaped teaspoon	6 g	24
BUTTER	10 g	74
LOW-FAT SPREAD	10 g	39
VERY LOW-FAT SPREAD	10 g	27
OIL		
1 teaspoon	3 ml	27
1 tablespoon	11 ml	100
BREAD		
1 medium wholemeal slice	36 g	77
wholemeal roll	48 g	116
RICE		
1 cooked portion – small	100 g	138
1 cooked portion – medium	180 g	248
1 cooked portion – large	290 g	400
PASTA		
1 cooked portion – small	150 g	156
1 cooked portion – medium	230 g	240
1 cooked portion – large	350 g	364

Food or drink	Quantity	Kcals
SPAGHETTI		
1 cooked portion – small	150 g	156
1 cooked portion – medium	220 g	229
1 cooked portion – large	270 g	281
POTATO		
1 baked with skin – small	100 g	136
1 baked with skin – medium	180 g	245
1 baked with skin – large	220 g	299
1 boiled, small	40 g	30
boiled, 1 portion – small	120 g	90
boiled, 1 portion – medium	175 g	131
boiled, 1 portion – large	220 g	165
WINE		
1 average glass dry white	125 ml	83
1 average glass red	125 ml	85
LAGER		
1/2 pt glass	287 ml	83
ORANGE JUICE		
(unsweetened) 1 small glass	160 ml	58
APPLE JUICE		
(unsweetened) 1 small glass	160 ml	61
APPLE 1 average-sized	112g	53
ORANGE		
1 average-sized	160 g	59
BANANA		
1 average-sized	100 g	95
PEANUTS		
1 handful (10)	13g	77
CRISPS		
1 small packet	28g	153
CHOCOLATE		
1 square	7g	37